THE
NEW YORKER
BOOK OF CAT CARTOONS

THE
NEW YORKER
BOOK OF CAT CARTOONS

BLOOMSBURY

First published in Great Britain 1990
Copyright © 1990 by The New Yorker Magazine, Inc.

The moral right of the author has been asserted

Bloomsbury Publishing Ltd, 2 Soho Square
London WIV 5DL

ISBN   0   7475   0788   0

A CIP catalogue record for this book is available
from the British Library

THE
NEW YORKER
BOOK OF CAT CARTOONS

"I know a lot of people will say 'Oh, no—not another book about cats.'"

1

"We had her declawed, but she's still impossible."

"Everyone be home by two o'clock!"

NEW, IMPROVED CAT

"*But when she got there, the cupboard was bare,
and so the poor dog had none.*"

"Guess what __we've__ done. We've just caught a mouse!"

"*I've never seen him pause next to anyone longer!*"

"*Your wife feels that your cat needs to hear an authoritative male voice.*"

"*Am I talking to <u>myself</u>?*"

"All right, darling, I promise. No more canned food."

"By the way, I've ordered a cat."

"*Makes you wonder, doesn't it?*"

"*From this day forward, we will do our <u>very</u> <u>best</u> to do unto Pussy as we would have Pussy do <u>unto</u> us.*"

O. SOGLOW

"This year I'm just going to give everybody kittens."

MOVIES FOR CATS

Fluffy Gets Fed

Yarn

Of Mice and Birds

R. Chast

*"One final question: Do you now own or have
you ever owned a fur coat?"*

ST.

ACT TAC ATC TCA CTA

"It's very simple. If I was a cat, you would love me."

"Before reading Miss Simpkins' will, may I say that you are a very lucky cat?"

"*Margo, I think it's time we talked about us.*"

1

2

3

4

"When she was little, we had a very close relationship,
but now we're just friends."

"*Around here his word is law.*"

"One morning they went out for a walk, and that's the last I ever saw of them."

"*I mean, God, Philip, what if he doesn't really <u>like</u> Tabby Treat but is only eating it so we'll feel less guilty?*"

"Are you all right?"

"*Of course some cats have eight kittens but I never have more than six.*"

"*We laugh at the same things.*"

"Mrs. Wallace _made_ me take them. She said
they were as much ours as theirs."

"Edgar, please run down to the shopping center right away, and get some milk and cat food. Don't get canned tuna, or chicken, or liver, or any of those awful combinations. Shop around and get a surprise. The pussies like surprises."

Front row: Smarty, Itty Fitty, Daisy, Boo, Mercedes, Foo Foo, Aka.
Second row: Spanky, Charlie, Mouse, Tigger, KiKi, Fluffy, Honey, Jerry.
Third row: Sweetheart, Pumpkin, B.J., Dennis, Emlyn, Pearl, Annie.
Back row: Miss Perringer.

"We're out of the cat food. Permit me to recommend the dog food."

47

"*If I take too many naps during the day, I find it difficult to sleep well at night.*"

"*Well, I hope you're proud of yourself!*"

BUDGIE DEFICIT

"He knows I can't stand it when he doesn't eat."

"I've enjoyed our little talk, and now I'll have
myself a nice little nap."

*"Like this—see? You've got to get
your back into it."*

"Is it all right for an expectant mother to catch chipmunks?"

"*All right, come out and we'll talk about it.*"

DIARY OF A CAT

TODAY

Today I got some food in a bowl. It was great! I slept some too.

TODAY

Played with yarn. Got some food in a bowl. Had a good nap.

TODAY

Slept, food, yarn. Fun!

TODAY

I played with a shoelace. Ate, slept. A good day.

TODAY

Slept. Ate some food. Yum.

TODAY

Food in a bowl. Yarn galore. Dozed for quite a while.

TODAY

Had a good nap. Then food in a bowl. Then yarn.

"The fact that you cats were considered sacred in ancient Egypt cuts no ice with me."

"*The patient in 12-C needs comforting.*"

"*I distinctly heard a bark.*"

"*And I can get along without you!*"

"Beg."

"She has her own agenda."

"*I tried to make it from the windowsill to the top of the refrigerator. How about you?*"

*"Well, sir, then I take it you would vote for any cat
in preference to a capable dog."*

73

"*I believe I've earned the right to your respect.*"

"Do you think a Siamese cat could tip it over?"

"And whose little mole is this?"

"*What do cats want?*"

"We have fourteen cats, but Kevin thinks we only have twelve."

"*Don't get cute with me.*"

Scaredy-Cats

CATS ARE NOT AS INTELLIGENT AS YOU THINK.

*"Glendora Hagan got in another load of cats,
Elinor honey. Can you take a couple?"*

"Both cats are mad at me."

"Now let's see—there's the Brosnahans, Mrs. Waldo, Arthur Elder,
the man at the A. & P. store. Now I wonder about Hannah Carpenter."

"Now, *don't start complaining till you taste it.*"

"I said you're in my light."

PUSS IN FACTORY SECONDS

"I'm a Cheshire mouse."

"Muffie's shedding."

"I'm sorry, but I think it's uncatlike."

"I do apologize, Rinehart. The cat has never bitten anyone previously."

"Hey, pal, let's hear 'Doggie in the Window' again, and this time play it like you mean it!"

"Miss Egan, bring me everything we have on cats."

Index of Artists

The text of this book was set in Caslon Old Face No. 2 at Kennedy Typographers, New York, New York. Printed and bound by Haliday Lithographers, West Hanover, Massachusetts.
Designed by Virginia Tan.